In the Name of
ALLAH
The Compassionate
and The Merciful

Library of Congress Catalog Card No. 82-70448
ISBN No. 0-89259-050-5

Published by American Trust Publications, USA

We Are Muslim Children

Songs and Verses for Muslim Girls and Boys

Compiled by Saida Chaudhry

American Trust Publications

Contents

Contents

How to Sing the Action Songs and Play the Games

Introduction

Dear Muslim Friends!
Assalamu-'alaikum!

I hope that you will like this book of Islamic songs, games and illustrations. It was created mainly with the Muslim child of the North American continent in mind. The North American Muslim Community is one of many cultures. We might wear different dresses, eat different food or speak different languages; but our goal ought to be that our children should outgrow cultural variances and find peace and fulfillment in the universal brother- and sisterhood that only Islam can bring.

Islam is a way of life. The earlier a Muslim child is introduced to Islamic values in his everyday activities, the better he will be prepared for his future life.

Songs and games have always appealed to children. It is a pleasant way to learn and relate. It may even lay the foundation for a life of happiness, faith and dignity, insha'-Allah.

Through the songs and verses I would like to convey the message to our Muslim children that Allah (S.W.T.), through His great Love and Mercy, has created us and the beautiful world in which we live. All our praise and worship is for Him alone!

Wa salamu-'alaikum!
Saida Chaudhry

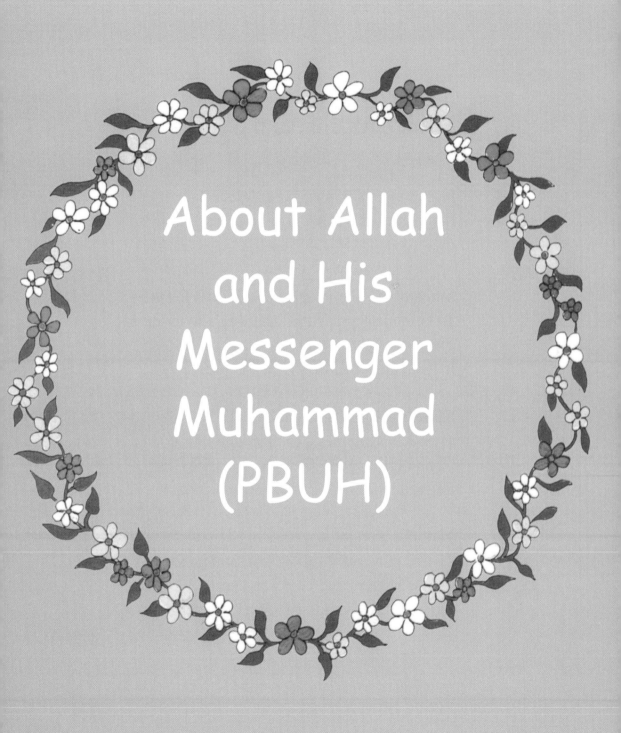

About Allah and His Messenger Muhammad (PBUH)

I Am a Muslim and God I Praise

I am a Muslim and God I praise,
For all His blessings my voice I raise.
In One God I believe, no equal has He.
Lord of the universe, compassionate to me.

Muhammad, the Prophet, taught me the way
To be honest and truthful throughout every day.
The Holy Qur'an through life is my guide,
Its teachings I follow, by it I abide.

Islam, my religion, teaches good deeds,
Mercy and kindness, to the right path it leads.
Upon all humanity God showers His Grace,
Regardless of color, nationality or race.

Through working together our hopes increase
To live in a world full of love and peace.
I am a Muslim and God I praise,
For all His blessings my voice I raise.

Praise Be To Allah

"Praise be to Allah!"
How often do we hear
The call of faithful Muslims
Resounding in our ears?

Allah alone we worship,
And to Him alone we pray.
God, make us Muslim children
Who follow in Your way.

The path of those You favor,
Not those who cause Your wrath.
O Allah, let our striving
Lead us to Your straight path.

Sustainer of the Universe,
Rabb al-'alameen, we pray,
Compassionate and Merciful,
Don't let us go astray.

All Creation Praises Allah

We Are Proud to be Muslims

We are all Muslims,
And we are proud.
Allahu Akbar!
Our call is loud.

We are all Muslims,
United by faith,
Together one ummah
in work and in play.

It makes no difference
Where we are from.
Helping each other,
We Muslims are one.

We are all Muslims,
Our live we would give.
Not for today
But for tomorrow we live.

We are all Muslims,
The hope of the world.
The message of Allah
Is what we have heard.

It makes no difference
Where we are from.
Helping each other,
We Muslims are one.

We are all Muslims,
The world we shall change,
Establish true justice,
Life rearrange.

We are the Muslims
Black, white and red.
By al-Qur'an and Sunnah
Our lives are led.

It makes no difference
where we are from.
Helping each other
    We Muslims are one.

When You Hear the Adhan Hurry for Prayer

La Ilaha IllAllah

Ya Allah hu, ya Allah,
We are Your servants, ya Allah!
La ilaha illAllah,
Muhummadur RasoolAllah.
I am but a Musselman,
My code of life is al-Qur'an.
I hear and honor the adhan,
And I will die a Musselman.
La ilaha illAllah,
Muhummadur RasoolAllah.

Ya Allah hu, ya Allah,
We are Your servants, ya Allah!
La ilaha illAllah,
Muhummadur RasoolAllah.
Each new day in Allah's Name,
Shun all things that bring You shame.
Do not follow what others say,
But practice all things in Allah's way.
La ilaha illAllah,
Muhummadur RasoolAllah.

Ya Allah hu, ya Allah,
We are Your servants, ya Allah!
La ilaha illAllah,
Muhummadur RasoolAllah.
Let Allah be your guiding light,
Be God-conscious day and night.
You'll be precious in His sight
If you follow His guiding light.
La ilaha illAllah,
Muhummadur RasoolAllah.

Ya Allah hu, ha Allah,
We are Your servants, ya Allah!
La ilaha illAllah,
Muhummadur RasoolAllah.
We must follow the Prophet's way,
Let satan lead us not astray.
Five times daily we must pray
And do good in Allah's way.
La ilaha illAllah,
Muhummadur RasoolAllah.

I Am a Muslim

I am a Muslim
And happy to say,
That I follow Allah's path
By night and by day.

It isn't always easy;
Sometimes it's quite hard.
But Allah will help me
If I do my part.

I try to pray five times a day,
As Allah said I should.
I wash myself after my play
He likes me to be good.

In Ramadan I try to fast
Just like my parents do,
And hope one day to go to hajj,
When I'm a grown-up too.

I do not fight with friends or shout
That's not the way to be;
I try to never sulk or pout
For Allah can see me.

I wash my hands before I eat;
I always should be clean;
And never ever do I steal
Because I know it's mean.

You see, I am a Muslim
And happy am I to say
That I am following Allah's path
By night and by day.

Eid Ul-Fitr

The month of fast has ended now,
O Muslims, join in praise!
Allah has given us al-Qur'an
To make us strong in faith.

The message that He sent to us,
O Muslims, heed the call —
Is that we live in brotherhood,
In peace and love with all.

The month of fast has ended now,
O Muslims, mind your souls.
The world's temptations we resist,
Islam is our goal.

Call of Islam

I'd like to build the world a mosque
And furnish it with faith,
For Africans and Chinamen
And every other race.

I'd like to see the world for once,
All praying side by side,
And hear them echo through the hills,
Islam throughout the land!

The call I hear,
That's the call of Islam,
That's the call of Iman,
It's the Word of God.

I'd like to teach the world the truth
And hear them praise our Lord,
To work and pray from day to day,
To earn their just reward.

I'd like to build the world a mosque
And furnish it with faith,
For Africans and Chinamen
And every other race.

The call I hear,
That's the call of Islam,
That's the call of Iman,
It's the Word of God.

Islam Throughout The Land

My Brother is Calling

Hassan, Hassan, will you come and follow me,
Will you come and follow me now?
Will you come and walk with me along Allah's path?
Hurry up and walk with me now.

> Yes, O brother, yes,
> Yes, O brother, yes;
> I will come and follow you,
> Follow you wherever you go.

Omar, Omar, will you come and follow me,
Will you come and follow me now?
Will you come and help me to spread Allah's word?
Hurry up and help me right now.

> Yes, O brother, yes,
> Yes, O brother, yes;
> I will come and follow you,
> Follow you wherever you go.

Muslim children, will you come and follow me
Will you come and follow me now?
Will you come and join me to praise Allah, our Lord?
Hurry up and join me right now.

> Yes, O brother, yes,
> Yes, O brother, yes;
> We will come and follow you,
> Follow you wherever you go.

Ya Ikhwan

Ahi ahi ya ikhwani, ahi ya ikhwan.
La ilaha illAllah, Muhammadur RasoolAllah.
Ahi ahi ya ikhwani, ahi ya ikhwan.

Five times daily prayer,
Also fasting in Ramadan.
Ahi ahi ya ikhwani, ahi ya ikhwan.

Giving Zakah is my duty —
To the poor it must be given.
Ahi ahi ya ikhwani, ahi ya ikhwan.

Once in a lifetime going to Mecca,
Performing Hajj, as a Muslim should.
Ahi ahi ya ikhwani, ahi ya ikhwan.

There is No god but One God

There is no god but One God
LA ILAHA ILLALLAH;
His Messenger Muhammad,
MUHAMMADUR RASOOLLALLAH.

When I drink and when I eat
I start with BISMILLAH,
And when my work is all complete
I say AL-HAMDU LILLAH.

When I promise to be good
I say INSHA' ALLAH.
I will do my best and try
O HELP ME, YA ALLAH.

A Muslim

Since I am a Muslim,
I always should be keen
To keep my heart and tongue pure
And keep my body clean.

Assalamu-'Alaikum

Assalamu-'Alaikum, Wa-'alaikum Assalam.
Assalamu-'Alaikum, Wa-'alaikum Assalam.
When I arrive I say salam,
And when I leave I say salam.
Greeting is always part of Islam,
Assalamu-'Alaikum, Wa-'alaikum Assalam.

Allah is Great

(a round for 2 or 4 groups)

Allah
Is Great, is Great
And Merciful,
Praise be to Him.
Ameen, Ameen.

We Thank You, Allah

We thank You, O Allah, for the food we eat,
We thank You, O Allah, for the friends we meet.
We thank You, O Allah, for showing us the way
To be good and happy Muslim children day after day.

A Muslim Child's Prayer

Ya Allah, to You I pray
To You I pray five times a day.
Allah, to You I pray
And follow in Your way.

Take my heart so pure and true;
My love and praise is all for You.
Take my heart so pure and true
I give it all to You.

Ya Allah, to You I pray;
Watch over me by night and day.
Allah, to You I pray
And follow in Your way.

Allah Loves Those Who Are
Constant in Prayer

Allah is Great

Allah is Great,
      Allahu Akbar!
And Powerful,
      Allahu Akbar!
He made the world,
      Allahu Akbar!
And all the stars,
      Allahu Akbar!
We pray to Him,
      Allahu Akbar!

Evening

The day has come to an end
And our prayers we send
To Allah kind and great.
May He bless our night
And keep us safe and right
And lead us all to Paradise.

The moon is shining bright,
The stars emit their light
From worlds so far away,
Allah is the Creator —
We bow before our Maker
And say la ilaha illAllah.

About Us
and
the Life Around

Heaven Wide

Heaven wide, sunshine bright,
Tell who is your master.
Praise Allah, He is the One
Who has given you the Holy Qur'an.

Meadows around, flowers abound,
Tell who gives you beauty.
Praise Allah, He is the One
Who has given you the Holy Qur'an.

Ocean wide, ebb and tide,
Tell who gives you orders.
Praise Allah, He is the One
Who has given you the Holy Qur'an.

Earth and Heaven

Earth and heaven, night and day,
Moon's soft light and sun's golden ray.
Earth and heaven, night and day,
Allah made for you and me.

Birds and bees, flowers and trees,
Animals on land and fishes in the seas.
Birds and bees, flowers and trees,
Allah made for you and me.

Summer, winter, fall and spring,
Seasons flying on the wing.
Summer, winter, fall and spring,
Allah made for you and me.

All Beautiful Things Are Created by Allah

Little Friends in Other Lands

Little friends in other lands,
I love you, I love you.
Little friends in other lands
Allah loves you too.

North or south or east or west,
I love you, I love you.
North or south or east or west,
Allah loves you too.

Allah Loves The Children

Allah loves the children,
Children everywhere.
Red or yellow, black or white,
They are precious in His Sight.
Allah loves the children,
Children everywhere.

Allah Loves Children

Look At Me

Look at me!
Can you see?
I am a Muslim child,
Happy as can be.

Allah's my Guide,
By day and night.
He loves me and cares for me
And makes my life bright.

Look at me!
Can you see?
I am a Muslim child,
happy as can be.

Allah Wants Us To Be Happy

Love One Another

Love one another,
Love one another,
Love one another,
This is Allah's way.

Help one another,
Help one another,
Help one another,
This is Allah's way.

Share with one another,
Share with one another,
Share with one another,
This is Allah's way.

Pray with one another,
Pray with one another,
Pray with one another,
This is Allah's way.

We Thank You, Ya Allah

For all the things
We have today;
For all our friends
We love so much;
For homes, for food,
For work and play,
We thank You,
Ya Allah.

Allah's Plan

Flower in a flower bed,
Growing bigger every day,
Sun and water help you grow,
Allah planned that way.

Little moth in a cocoon,
You'll wake up one warm spring day,
After sleeping all winter through,
Allah planned that way.

Autumn leaves are turning brown,
Wind is blowing them away.
See them whirling, whirling down,
Allah planned that way.

I Wonder

I wonder, I wonder —
I wonder about the birds
That fly so high.
Allah sends the birds up in the sky.

I wonder, I wonder —
I wonder about the sun
That shines so bright.
Allah sends the sun to give us light.

I wonder, I wonder —
I wonder about the moon
That shines at night.
Allah gave the moon a silvery light.

I wonder, I wonder —
I wonder about the wind
That blows OO-ooo.
All comes from Allah
For He loves us so.

When I Get Up in the Morning

When I get up in the morning,
My heart is filled with joy;
A new day Allah made for me,
Allahu Akbar.

My days are filled with sunshine,
With friends and playtime too;
Guide me along the path that's
    straight,
Allahu Akbar.

At night when the moon is shining,
The world is quiet and still.
I thank You for the rest You give,
Allahu Akbar.

And all through my lifetime
I'll follow Allah's way.
My wish is to be close to You,
Allahu Akbar.

Every New Day
is a Gift From Allah

Good Deeds

Allah loves children
Who care for others,
Who do deeds of kindness
To sisters and brothers;

Like lending a hand
To somebody hurt,
Like smiling at him
And saying a kind word;

Like happily sharing
With girls and with boys
One's favorite things
Like books and like toys;

Like sending flowers to somebody ill;
A visit to him
Would be nicer still.

There are many things
We can do for each other,
To make life happy
For our sister or brother.

Kindness Pleases Allah

Allah's Gifts

I use my hands to feel,
I use my eyes to see.
Allah gave me ears to hear
The birds up in the tree.

I use my tongue to taste
The food He gave to me.
Allah gave me a nose to smell
The blossoms on the tree.

My Name is Aisha

Do you know my name is Aisha,
Is Aisha, is Aisha?
Do you know my name is Aisha,
And what is your name?

I Travel to Mecca

I travel far to Mecca town;
Who wants to come with me?
And you, o my dear brother,
Won't you follow me?

We have arrived in Mecca now;
We've come so very far.
We have come here to bow and pray
Allahu Akbar!

Sugar Donuts

Five sugar donuts
In the baker's shop,
Big and round
With icing on the top.
Along came Saima
With a penny one day.
She bought a sugar donut
and she ate it right away.

Halal, haram, halal, haram —
Some are not good for us.
The one she bought
And quickly ate,
You tell me what it was!

The Muezzin

See the muezzin climbing up the minaret?
He calls to Muslim people
Who are sleeping in their bed.
He says: "It's time for prayer,
Too much sleep is in vain."
And after he has finished,
He is climbing down again.

Brother Hassan

This is Brother Hassan in his bed;
He hears the call for prayer from the minaret.
He dresses in a hurry,
He does not waste his time,
To say his prayer at the mosque
With brothers in a straight line.

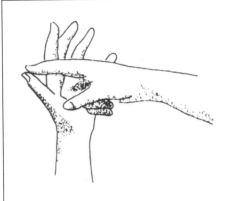

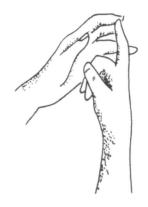

I Have Five Fingers

I have five fingers on my hand.
They all stand up to say,
One, two, three
Four, five times a day
A Muslim has to pray.

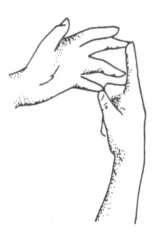

FAJR

DHUHR

'ASR

MAGHRIB

'ISHA

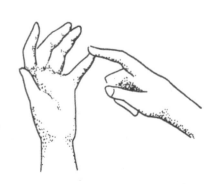

Eid Is a Time for Celebration

Baking Cookies for Eid

I am making cookie dough,
Round and round the beaters go.
I add some flour from a cup,
Then stir and stir the batter up.

I roll them, cut them nice and neat
And put them on a cookie sheet.
I bake them, count them —
One, two, three;

And I serve them on Eid
To my Muslim friends,
When they drop in
After prayer for tea.

Allah the Creator Made You and Me

This is the sun with rays so bright;
This is the moon that shines at night.
This is a bird with feathered wing,
And this is a bee that has a sting.
This is a bunny with ears so long,
And this is me, all healthy and strong.
Do you know how everything happened to be?
Allah the Creator made you and me.
He made the bunny, the bird and the bee
And everything around us that you can see.

Five Muslim Children

Five Muslim children
Are going out to play.
They call on five Muslim friends
Living down the way.
They greet: "Assalamu-'alaikum,"
"Wa-'alaikum Assalam!"
And quickly they run home again,
When they hear from the mosque the adhan.

Let's Go Around and Sing a Song

Let's go around and sing a song,
Sing a song, sing a song;
Let's go around and sing a song,
For we are Muslim children.

This is the way we wash our hands,
Wash our hands, wash our hands;
This is the way we wash our hands
Before every meal.

We sit down to eat and say "Bismillah,"
"Bismillah," "Bismillah,"
We sit down to eat and say "Bismillah"
And "Thanks to Allah" too.

And now it's time to play and run,
Play and run, play and run;
And now it's time to play and run
Until it's time to pray.

We wash our hands and face and feet,
To say salat, to say salat;
We wash our hands and face and feet
Five times a day.

When the sun goes down it's time for bed;
It's time for bed, it's time for bed;
When the sun goes down it's time for bed.
Good night all Muslim children.

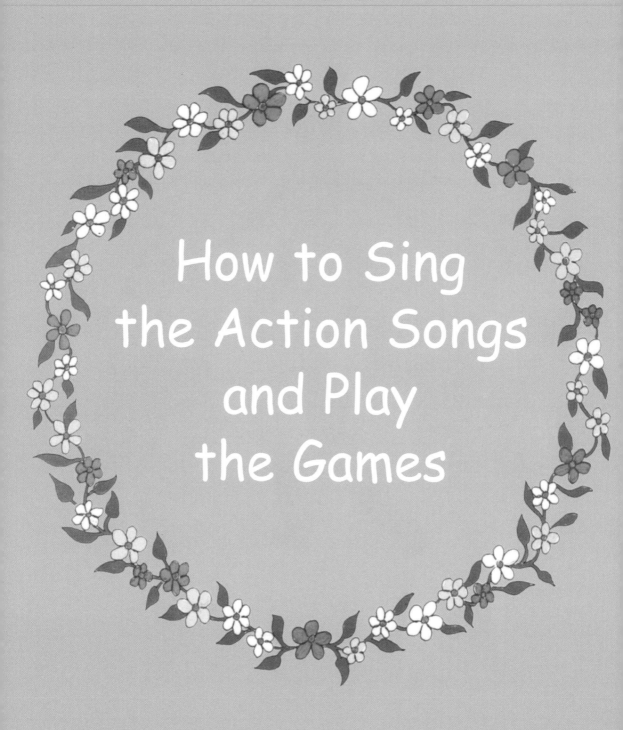

How to Sing
the Action Songs
and Play
and Play
the Games

Assalamu-'Alaikum — Page 14

Children are divided into two groups. One group starts singing "Assalamu-'alaikum," while the other returns the greeting "Wa'alaikum assalam." The two groups finish the song together.

Allah is Great — Page 14

A child picked by the teacher as the leader recites "Allah is great" and the group chants "Allahu Akbar." He/she makes a big circle for the world, points up at stars and looks down at open hands for prayer, while the group keeps on chanting "Allahu Akbar." This little verse is suitable for 4-6 year olds.

Earth and Heaven — Page 18

At the lines "Allah made for you and me," the children point first at a friend and then themselves.

Look at Me — Page 22

While singing "Look at me," the children point to themselves, and whey they sing "I am a Muslim child," they clap their hands joyfully.

Good Deeds — Page 26

A little game to teach children to be kind and helpful. A child is chosen by the teacher. This child can pick his or her partner, to whom he/she does a kind deed, such as wiping away tears, buttoning the coat, etc. The child in the group who guesses the action first is getting his/her turn and everyone guesses again.

My Name is Aisha — Page 28

This little introducing game can be used in conversation with the children about Muslim names and their meanings. Newcomers can introduce themselves in this way. The child stands up and sings "Do you know my name is . . .?" At the line "And what is your name?," he/she points at another child, who will sing the song all over again. Children like to play this game sitting in a circle, while the child in the middle slowly turns around, singing the song.

FINGER PLAYS

I Travel to Mecca — Page 29
A child picked by the teacher as the leader walks around while the group sings the song. At "and you, my dear brother, won't you follow me," the leader touches the child closest to him, who takes his hand and starts making a chain. Until all children are picked up, they sing the first verse over and over again. Of course for a sister they will change the wording. When all children are picked, the chain stops and they all sing the second verse together. When arriving at the line, "bow and pray," the children raise their hands as if in prayer. After they have shouted "Allahu Akbar," the game can start all over again. This is a good game for outdoors, because there is more space, and the chain of children can wind around trees, picnic tables, etc.

Sugar Donuts — Page 29
Five "sugar donuts," circles cut out of colorful construction paper with a hole in the middle, are placed on the floor. Each has a different color. The teacher announces that the "green donut," for example, is haram and forbidden for us to eat.

The group is singing the song while the child, who was picked by the teacher, skips to the "donuts," picks his/her choice and pretends to eat it. The group sings "halal, haram . . ." and at the line "you tell me, what it was?," the teacher points at a child who has to guess. Whoever guesses right will have the next choice of donuts. If the group is larger, more "donuts" can be used, and maybe more colors could be "haram." This game is suitable for 4-6 year olds.

The Muezzin — Page 30
Pointer and middle fingers of right hand are climbing up left inner forearm. "He says: 'It's time for prayer,'" fold fingers of left hand over and let the pointer stick out between them. After finishing his call, the pointer is climbing down the arm again.

Brother Hassan — Page 30
Put pointer of right hand into palm of left hand for Brother Hassan's bed. Folding over him three fingers for a bed cover. He jumps out of bed when

hearing the call for prayer and dresses in a hurry, turning around several times. Both hands line up straight for prayer.

I Have Five Fingers — Page 31
The child makes a fist with the right hand. At the line, "They all stand up to say," all five fingers pop up and stand straight. With the left hand, the child counts fingers, one two three, four, five, and again the same fingers, Fajr, Dhuhr, 'Asr, Maghrib and 'Isha.

Baking Cookies for Eid — Page 33
Make actions corresponding to rhyme.

Allah the Creator Made You and Me — Page 34
Sun — spread fingers wide.
Moon — circle with fingers of both hands.
Bird — cross hands at wrists and wiggle fingers (for wings).
Bee — fist with finger pointing out (for sting).
Bunny — fist with 2 fingers pointing straight up (for ears).
Me — pointing at self.
You and me — pointing at friend and self.
Bunny, bird and bee — actions as above.
Everything around — big circle with both arms.

Five Muslim Children — Page 35
Lift up five fingers of right hand. When "They call on," lift up fingers of left hand (for friends). Both hands face each other. They bend forward to greet, first with the right, then with the left hand, when saying "Assalamu-'alaikum" and "Wa-'alaikum Assalam." Fingers disappear in fist for running home quickly. Lift both hands to ears for adhan.

Let's Go Around and Sing a Song — page 36
"Let's go around and sing a song," children are skipping around in a circle.
"This is the way we wash our hands," action of washing hands.
"We sit down to eat," all sit down.
"and 'Thanks to Allah' too," children pretending to eat.
"And now it's time to play and run," children are getting up from the floor,

they are making a circle again and skip around.

"We wash our hands and face and feet," actions of washing.

"When the sun goes down it's time for bed," the children are going slowly down to the floor and they are pretending to sleep.

To get the children up from the floor, the teacher claps her hands and again sings, "Let's go around and sing a song." The children form another circle and usually end up laughing.

Acknowledgments

I wish to express my gratitude to all who have helped in the compilation of this book, especially the Muslim children, who are the source of my inspiration.

I am grateful to the unknown authors of the following songs, which are much loved by the Muslim children: "I Am a Muslim," "La Ilaha IllAllah," "There is No god but One God," "Since I Am a Muslim," "Assalamu-Alaikum," "Ya Ikhwan," and "Call to Islam." Very special thanks are due to Sisters Mohja Kahf and Salimah Siddiqui for their poem, "We Are All Muslims," for which I made a melody; and to Sister Khatija Haffajee, without whose moral support and encouragement this book might not have been printed. Artists Pamela Howell, Khalid Dow and my neighbour Olga Earwaker have made the book colorful with their illustrations. Last, but not least, I like to thank the lovely young sisters Sofia Ansari, Shereen Tareen and Sadia Omar for helping me to materialize the tape.

Above all we praise Allah (S.W.T.) for guiding us in our efforts; and we pray that He might bless this project — a small effort indeed in His cause — that it might bring spiritual rewards.

S.C.